How to use this book

Follow the advice, in italics, given for you on each page.
***Praise** the children at every step!*

Detailed guidance is provided in the Read Write Inc. Phonics Handbook.

7 reading activities

Children:

- ☆ *Practise reading the speed sounds.*
- ☆ *Read the green and red words for the Ditty.*
- ☆ *Listen as you read the introduction.*
- ☆ *Read the Ditty.*
- ☆ *Re-read the Ditty and discuss the 'questions to talk about'.*
- ☆ *Re-read the Ditty with fluency and expression.*
- ☆ *Practise reading the speed words.*

Speed Sounds

Consonants

Say the pure sounds (do not add 'uh').

f	l	m	n	r	s	v	z	(sh)	(th)	ng nk

b	c k	d	g	h	j	p	qu	t	w	x	y	(ch)

Vowels

Say the sounds in and out of order.

a	e	i	o	u

Each box contains only one sound. Focus sounds are circled.

Ditty 1 Got him

Green words

Read in Fred Talk (pure sounds).

van him yuk got

mud in shed

Red words

the

Ditty 1 Got him

Introduction

Do you like playing hide and seek? At the start of the story, the children are looking for places to hide. What places might they choose?

1 2 3 4 5 6 7 8 9... 10

in the van

got him

in the shed

got him

in the mud
got him...

yuk

Ditty 2 Mix it up

Green words

Read in Fred Talk (pure sounds).

big mix top chop yum

it a in up dish this on

Read in syllables.

sa\`lad → salad

Red words

I put

Ditty 2 # Mix it up

Introduction

This is a story about a cook making a tasty meal.

I chop it up

I put it in a big dish

I mix it up

I put this on top

salad

yum yum

Ditty 3 In the bin

Green words

Read in Fred Talk (pure sounds).

bag rug hat bin in

this lid on

Red words

the put

Ditty 3 In the bin

Introduction

In this story the children help Mum tidy up . . . but there's a problem!

put <u>th</u>is bag in <u>th</u>e bin

put this hat in the bin

put this rug in
the bin

put the lid on...

Questions to talk about

Ditty 1

Where is the first boy hiding?

Which hiding place do you think is the best?

Where do you hide when you play hide and seek?

Ditty 2

What does the cook do first?

Do you think the cook likes the salad?

What is your favourite vegetable?

Ditty 3

What is the second thing that Mum asks the boy to put in the bin?

Why can't they put the lid on the bin?

What sort of things do you put in the bin?

Speed words for Ditty 1

Children practise reading the words across the rows, down the columns and in and out of order clearly and quickly.

in	yuk	shed	van
got	him	the	mud

Speed words for Ditty 2

mix	on	dish	big	up
chop	it	a	top	this

Speed words for Ditty 3

on	bag	the	hat	bin
put	rug	this	in	lid